THE Kew Gardens
ENCHANTING COLOURING BOOK

THE Kew Gardens

ENCHANTING COLOURING BOOK

OVER 50
BEAUTIFUL
IMAGES

ARCTURUS

Kew
Royal Botanic Gardens

All illustrations included in this book have been taken
from the Library, Art & Archives Collections of the Royal
Botanic Gardens, Kew.

Special thanks to everyone at Kew Publishing, Lynn
Parker, Art and Illustrations Curator, and Dr Martyn Rix,
Editor of *Curtis's Botanical Magazine*.

Plant Names
The key on pages 6–19 uses the original names by which
the plants and flowers were first known when these
illustrations were made.

ARCTURUS

This edition published in 2020 by Arcturus Publishing Limited
26/27 Bickels Yard, 151–153 Bermondsey Street,
London SE1 3HA

ISBN: 978-1-78950-163-6
CH006917NT
Supplier 29, Date 0420, Print run 10339

Printed in China

Created for children 10+

Introduction

Flowers create feelings of happiness and well-being and also denote meanings – a white rose for pure love, an hibiscus for delicate beauty, and a tulip for forgiveness. For everyone who loves flowering plants and would like to make pictures that capture their grace and charm, this colouring book is perfect.

The artworks in this book are taken from the legendary archive of *Curtis's Botanical Magazine*. Founded in 1787 and originally named *The Botanical Magazine* by apothecary and Kew Gardens botanist William Curtis (1746–99), the periodical went on to become the longest-running magazine featuring colour illustrations of plants in the world.

A variety of highly talented artists produced hand-coloured copper plate engravings for the magazine, and the artworks featured in this book draw principally on those of the famous Scottish botanical illustrator Walter Hood Fitch (1817–92), but also include a few illustrations by Matilda Smith (1854–1926), Kew's first official botanical artist, and one by Harriet Anne Thiselton-Dyer (1854–1945), an accomplished botanical illustrator and daughter of the famous botanist and explorer Joseph Dalton Hooker.

Presented in this compilation are more than 50 colour plates of flowers together with their corresponding black and white line illustrations for you to colour in. Join the popular renaissance in the art of botanical illustration and start right here by taking a pencil or paintbrush and colouring in your first petals and leaves. With plenty of variety and detail to keep you busy, this book will inspire you to start your own wonderful library of enchanting flowers from Kew Gardens.

KEY: LIST OF PLATES

1 *Podocarpus neriifolia*

2 *Lindenia rivalis*

3 *Rhodanthe manglesii*

4 *Saccolabium miniatum*

5 *Berberis darwini*

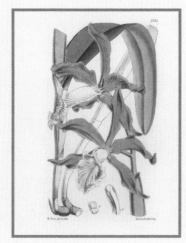

6 *Laelia grandis*

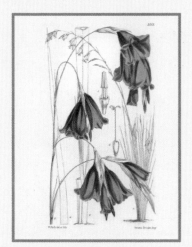

7 *Sparaxis pulcherrima*

8 *Higginsia regalis*

9 *Clintonia andrewsiana*

10 *Impatiens repens*

11 *Alloplectus capitatus*

12 *Tillandsia bulbosa*

13 *Coelogyne hookeriana*

14 *Epigynium acuminatum*

15 *Portlandia platantha*

16 *Grindelia grandiflora*

17 *Rosa alba L.*

18 *Lithospermum gastonii*

19 *Crinum giganteum*

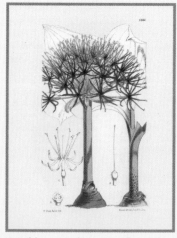

20 *Haemanthus tenuiflorus*

21 *Grevillea alpestris*

22 *Hibiscus radiatus*

23 *Lilium nepalense*

24 *Ada aurantiaca*

25 *Disa grandiflora*

26 *Rondeletia odorata*

27 *Iresine herbstii*

28 *Abelia floribunda*

29 *Primula parryi*

30 *Fuchsia simplicicaulis*

31 *Camellia reticulata*

32 *Curcuma cordata*

33 *Campanula fragilis*

34 *Rhododendron fortunei*

35 *Mutisia decurrens*

36 *Delphinium brunonianum*

37 *Spiraea douglasii*

38 *Bejaria coarctata*

39 *Agave glaucescens*

40 *Aucuba japonica*

41 *Acacia drummondii*

42 *Dendrobium devonianum*

43 *Alstromeria caldasii*

44 *Clomenocoma montana*

45 *Alocasia metallica*

46 *Nymphaea ampla*

47 *Columnea kalbreyeri*

48 *Tinnea aethiopica*

49 *Passiflora van-volxemii*

50 *Morenia fragrans*

51 *Yucca canaliculata*

52 *Cattleya schilleriana*

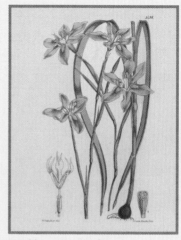

53 *Mamillaria clava* **54** *Vieussieuxia fugax*

1

1.   2.

2

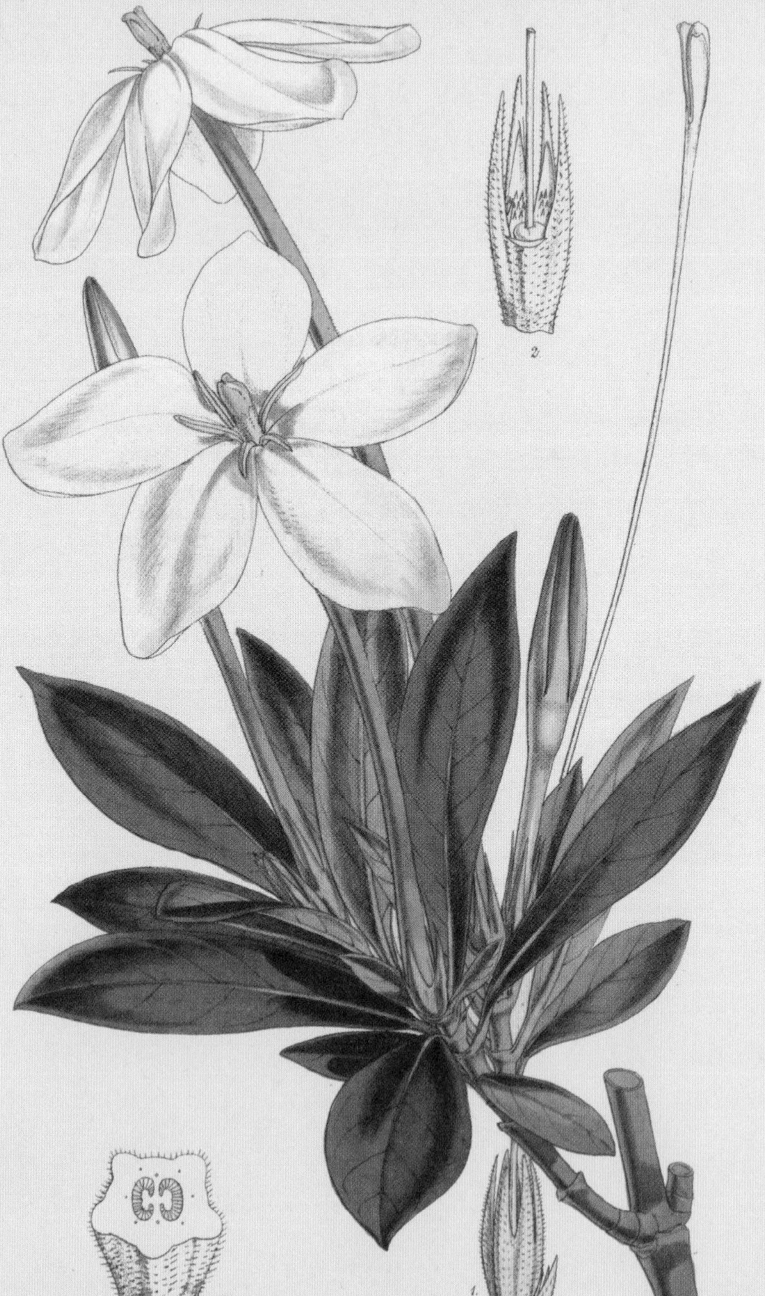

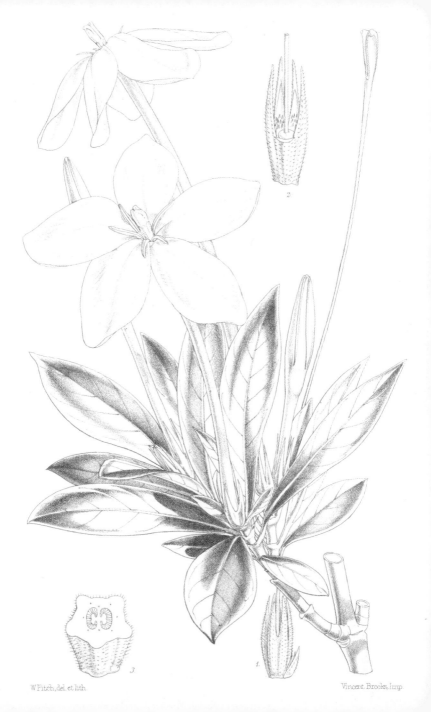

4

W.Fitch del. et lith.

Vincent.Brooks Imp.

1.

2.

3.

W. Fitch, del. et lith.

Vincent Brooks, Imp.

8

9

7092

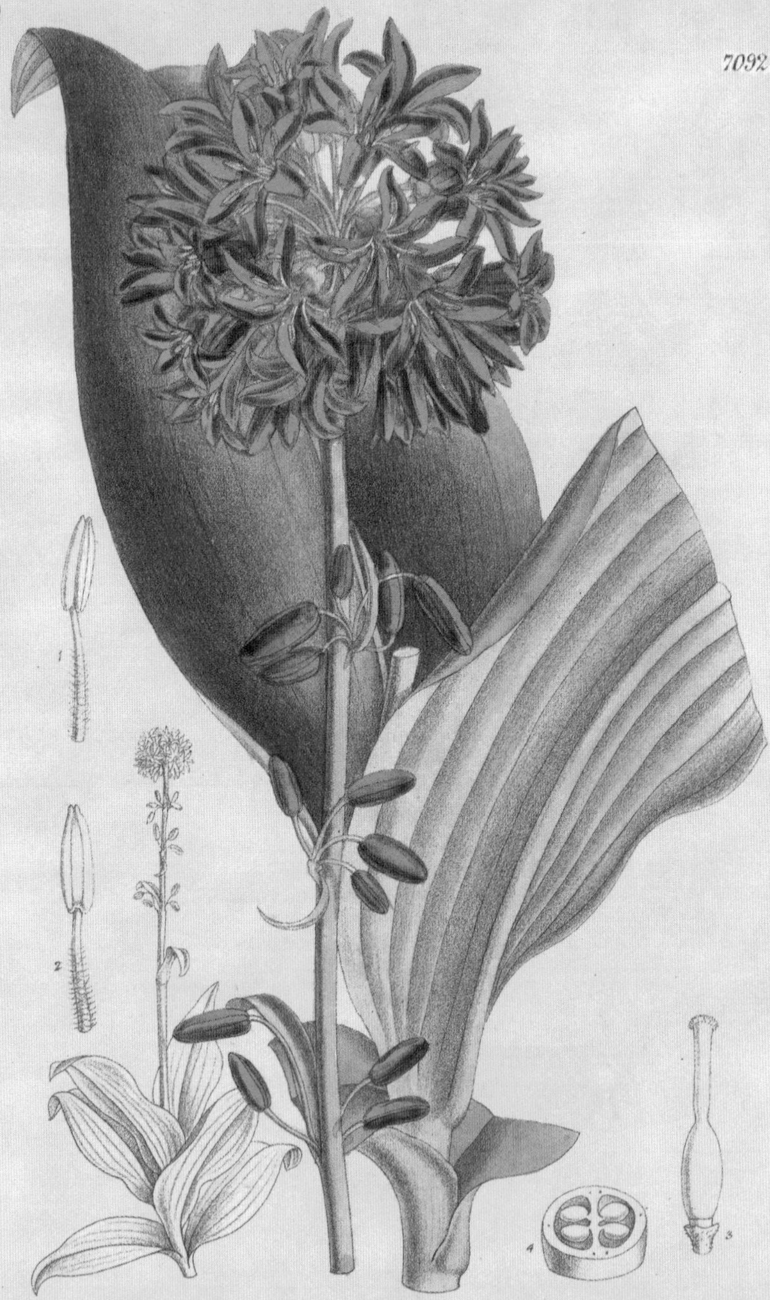

M.S. del, J.N. Fitch lith.

Vincent Brooks, Day & Son Imp

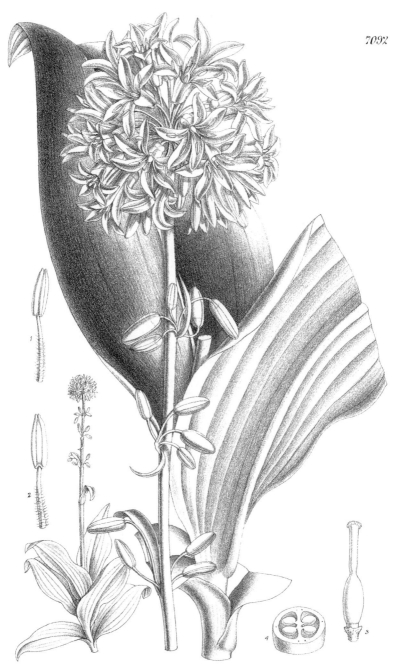

M.S.del, J.N.Fitch lith.

Vincent Brooks,Day & Son.Imp.

R. B & R. imp.

Fitch. del et lith.

R. B. & R. imp

4452.

12

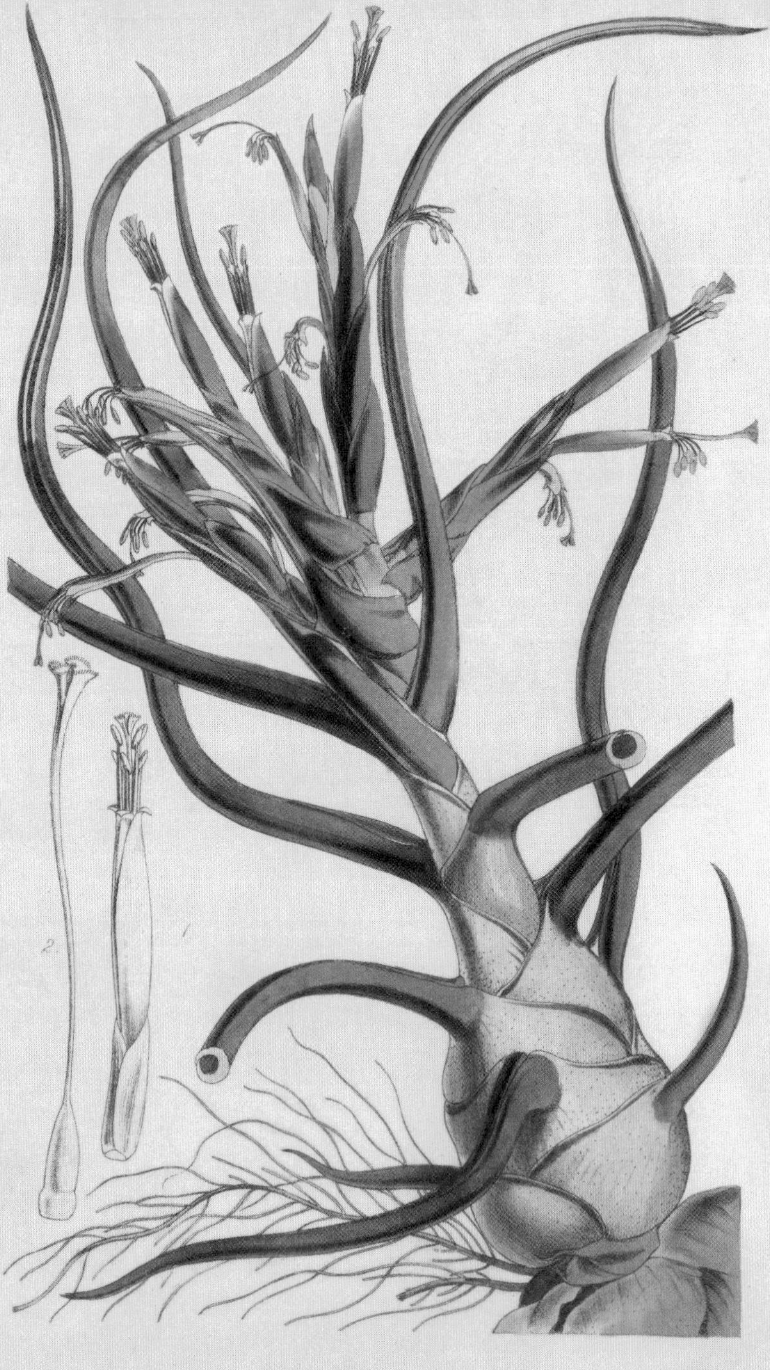

6388.

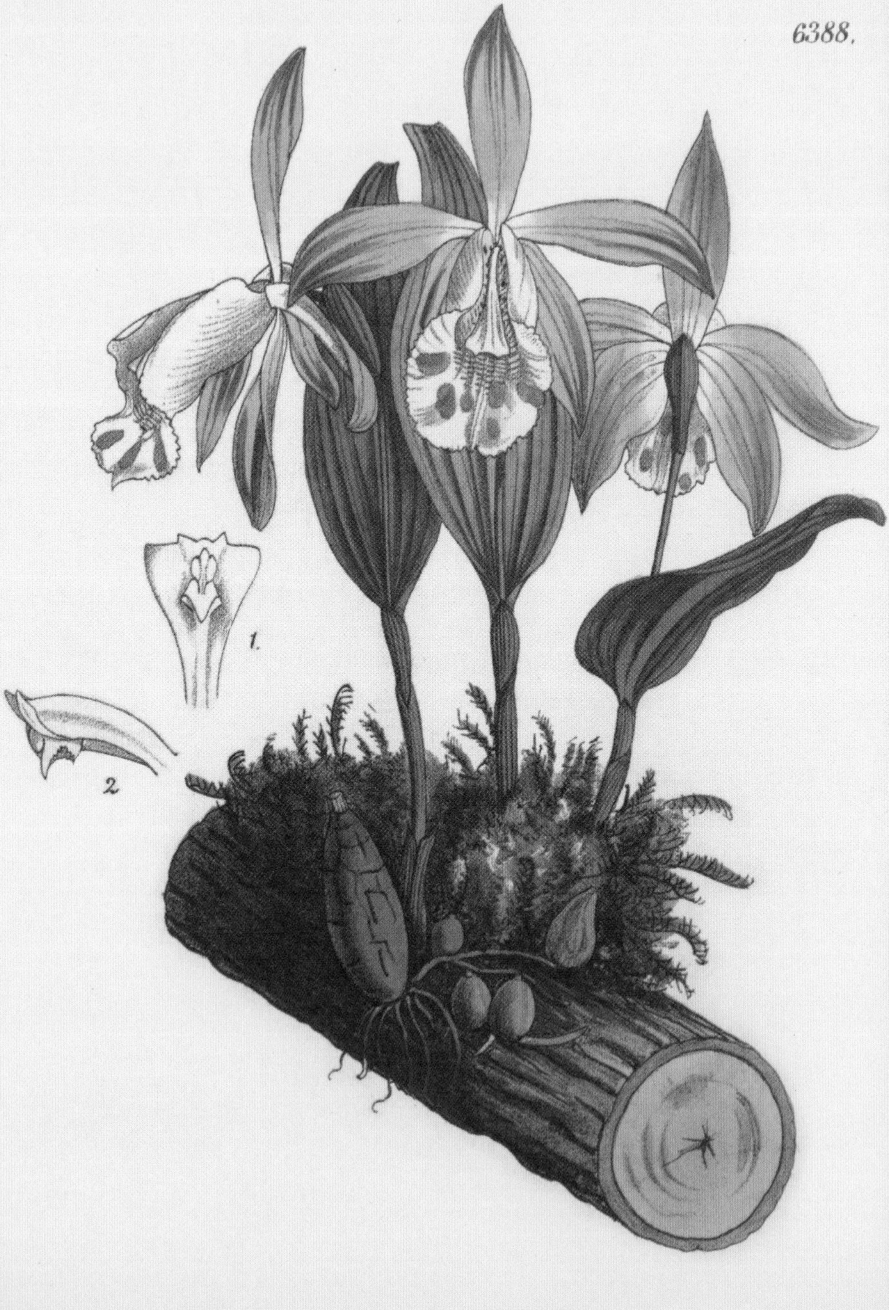

6388.

14

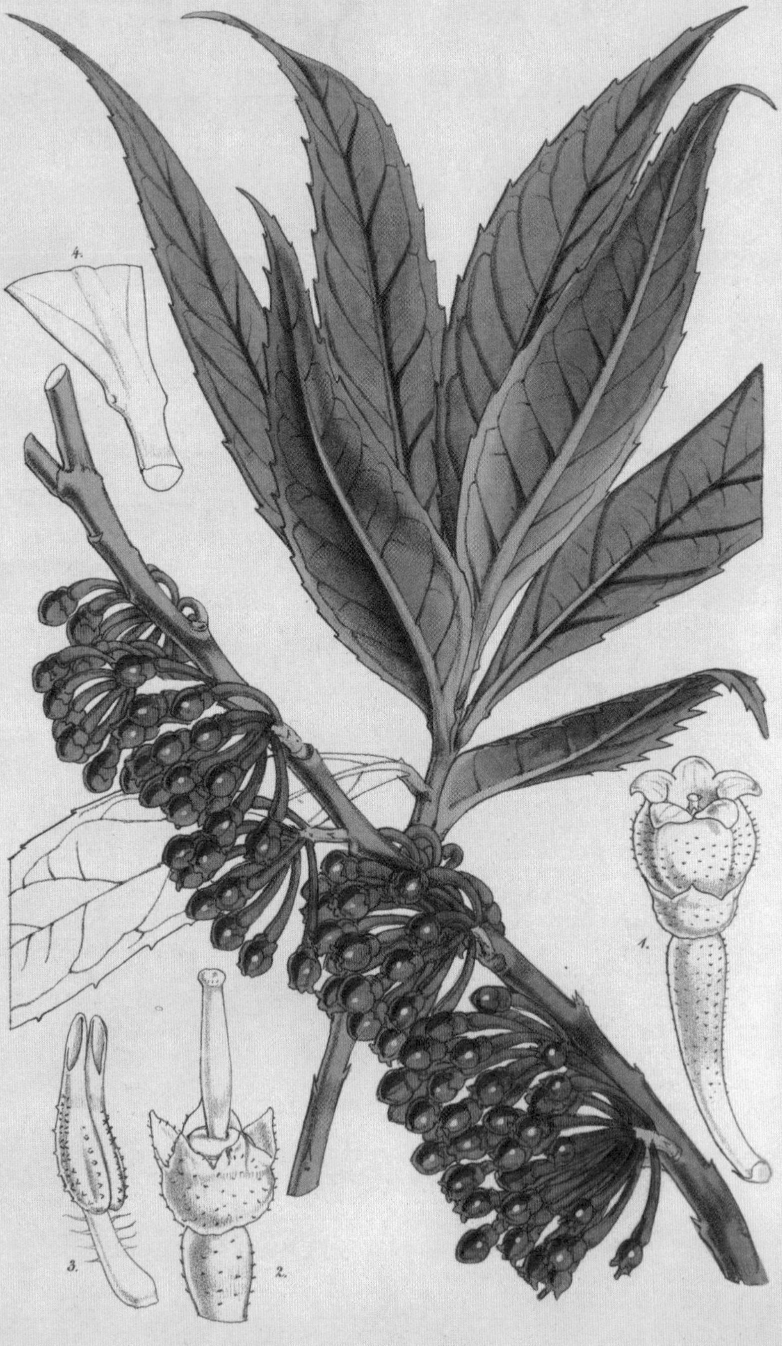

1.   *2.*   *3.*

1. 2. 3.

1.   2.   3.

17

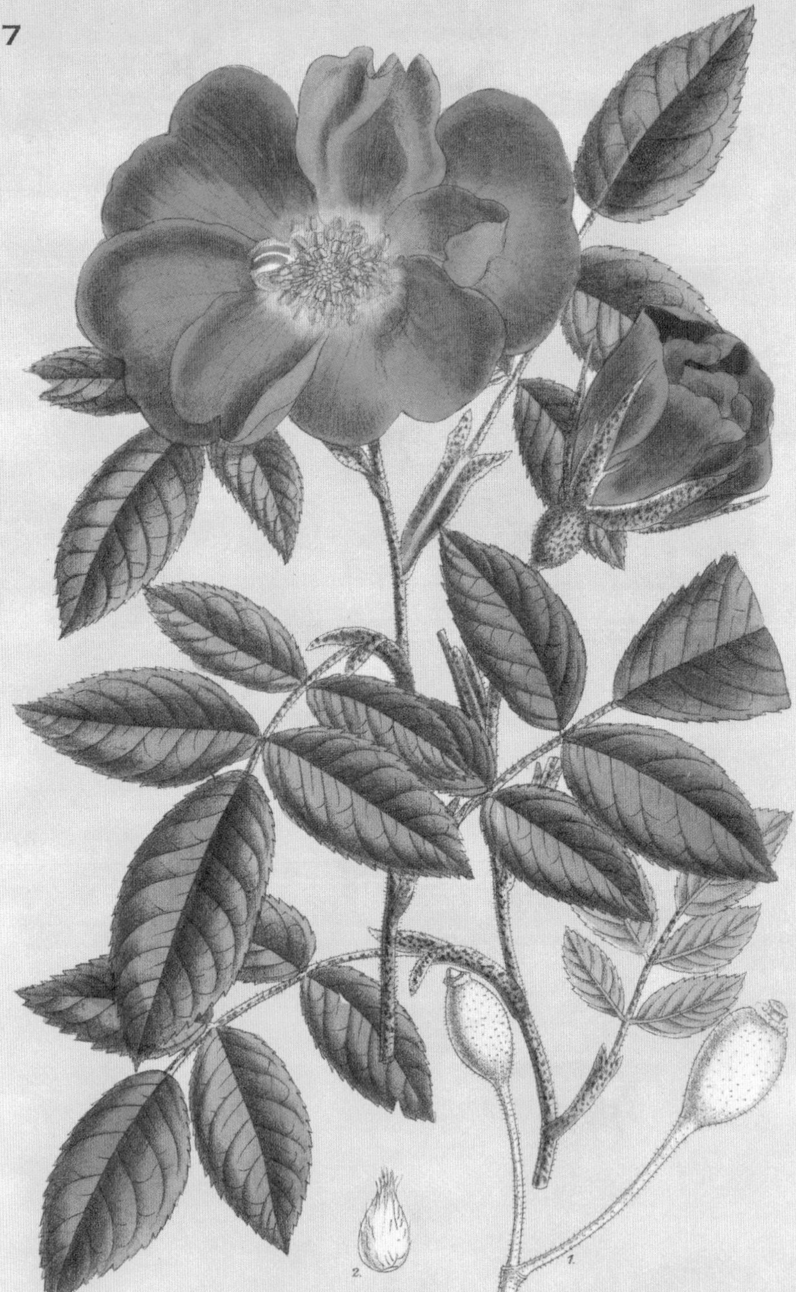

M.S. del, J.N. Fitch, lith.

Vincent Brooks, Day & Son, Imp

2.   1.

W.Fitch,del.et lith.

Vincent Brooks,Imp.

1.

2.

3.

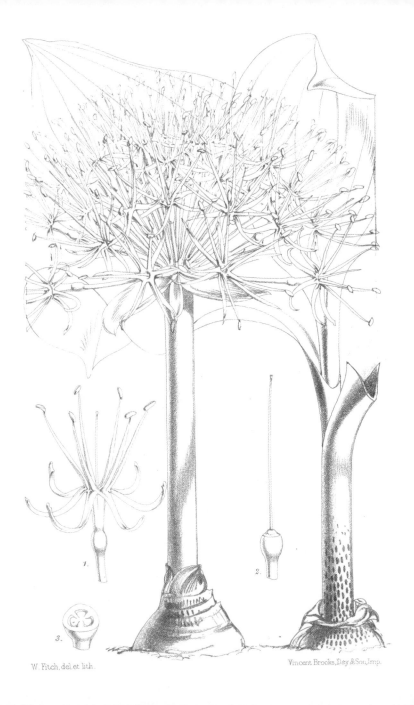

21

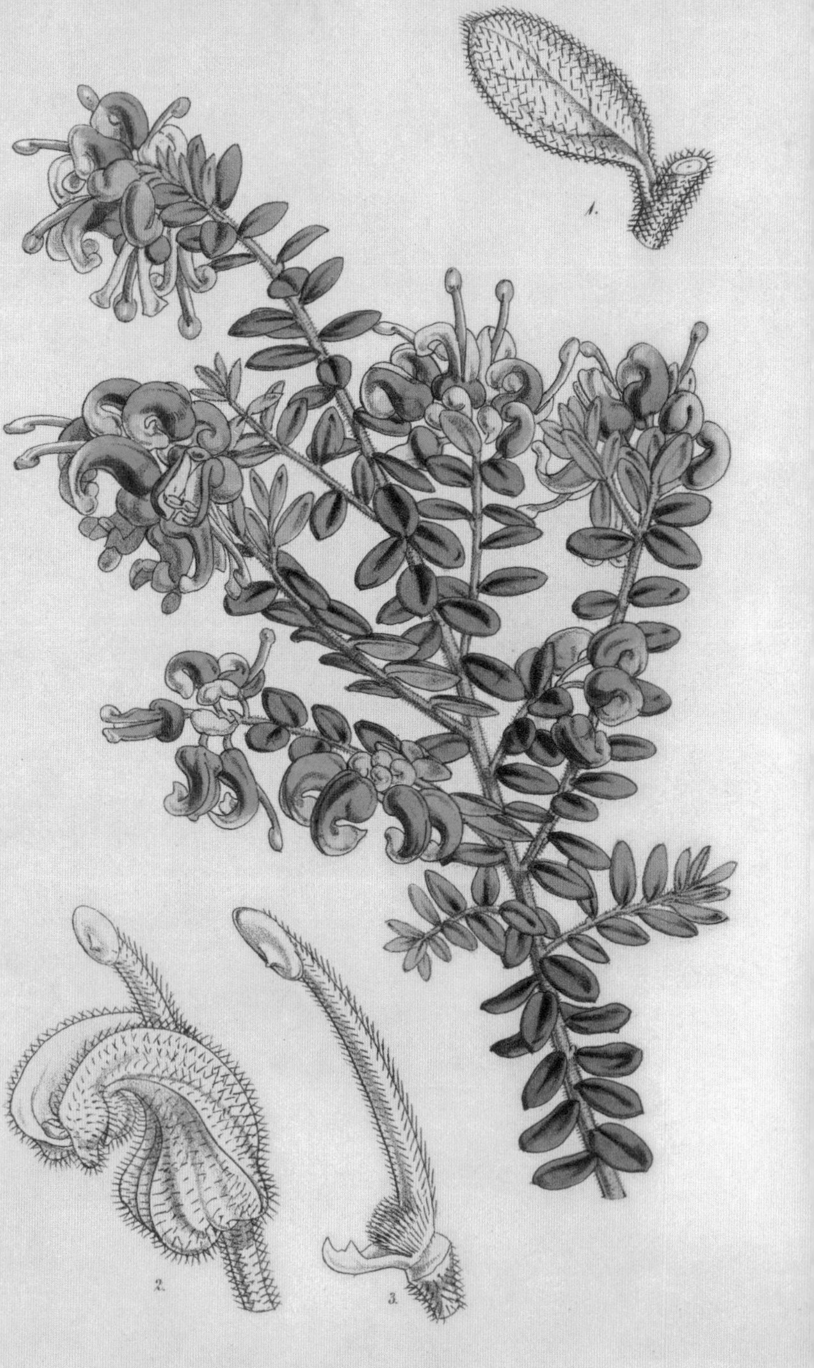

W.Fitch, del. et lith.

Vincent Brooks, Imp.

W. Fitch, del. et lith.

Vincent Brooks, Imp.

Vincent Brooks,Day & Son Imp

W.Fitch, del.et lith.

Vincent Brooks,Imp.

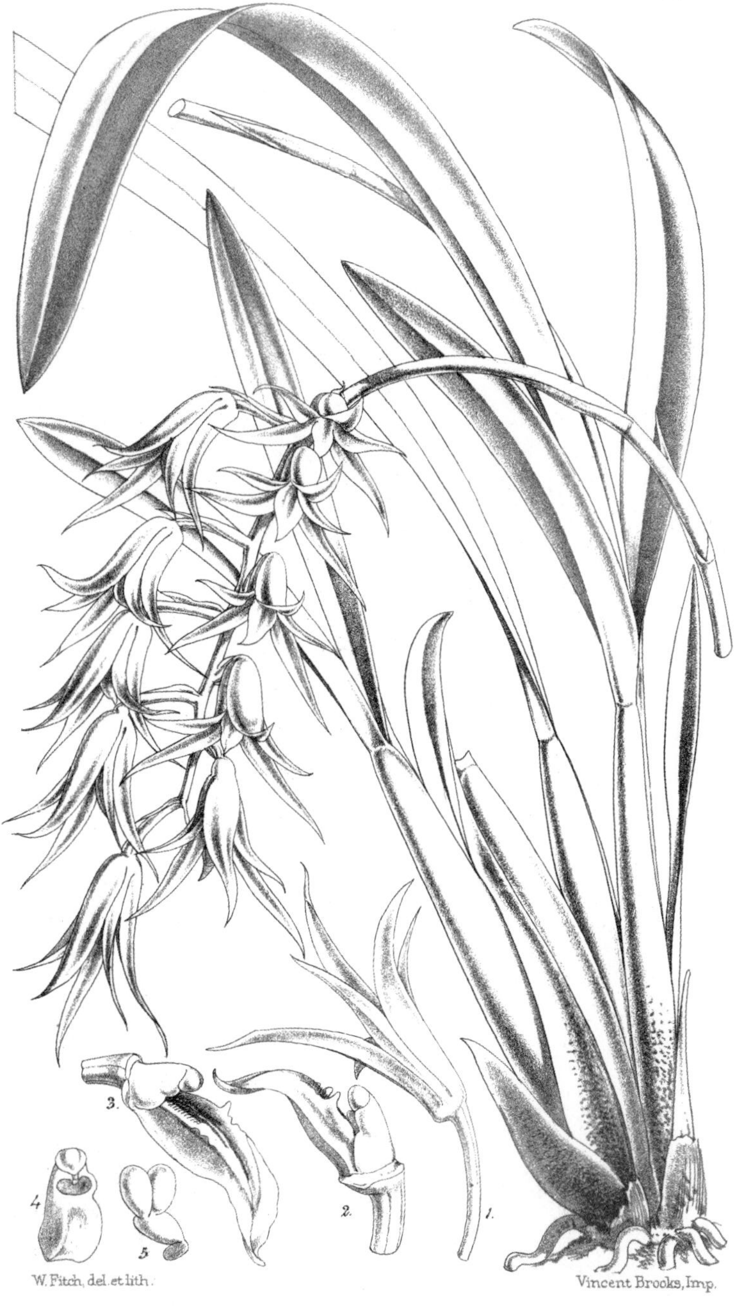

W. Fitch, del. et lith.

Vincent Brooks, Imp.

4073.

4073.

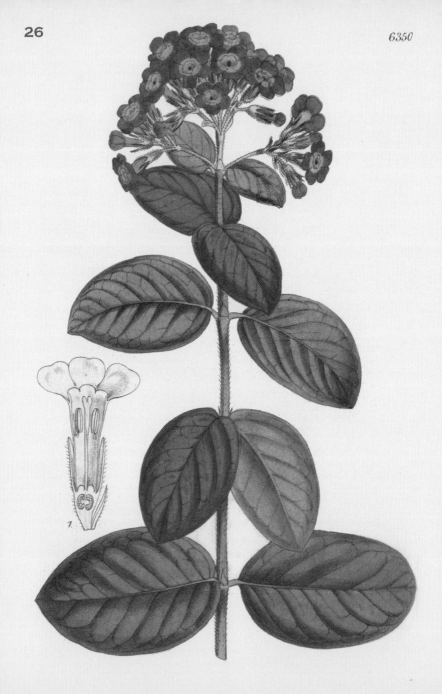

1.

2.

2.

1.   2.   3.

1.   2.   3.

W Fitch del et lith

Vincent Brooks Day & Son Imp

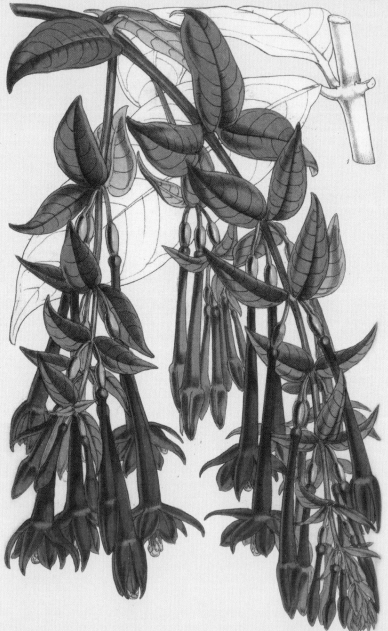

Vincent Brooks, Imp.

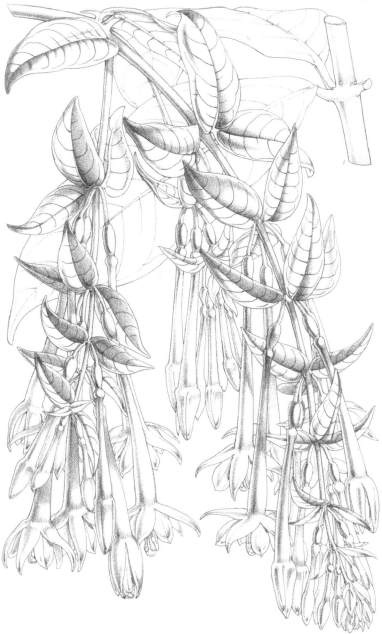

W. Fitch, delt. et lith.

Vincent Brooks, Imp.

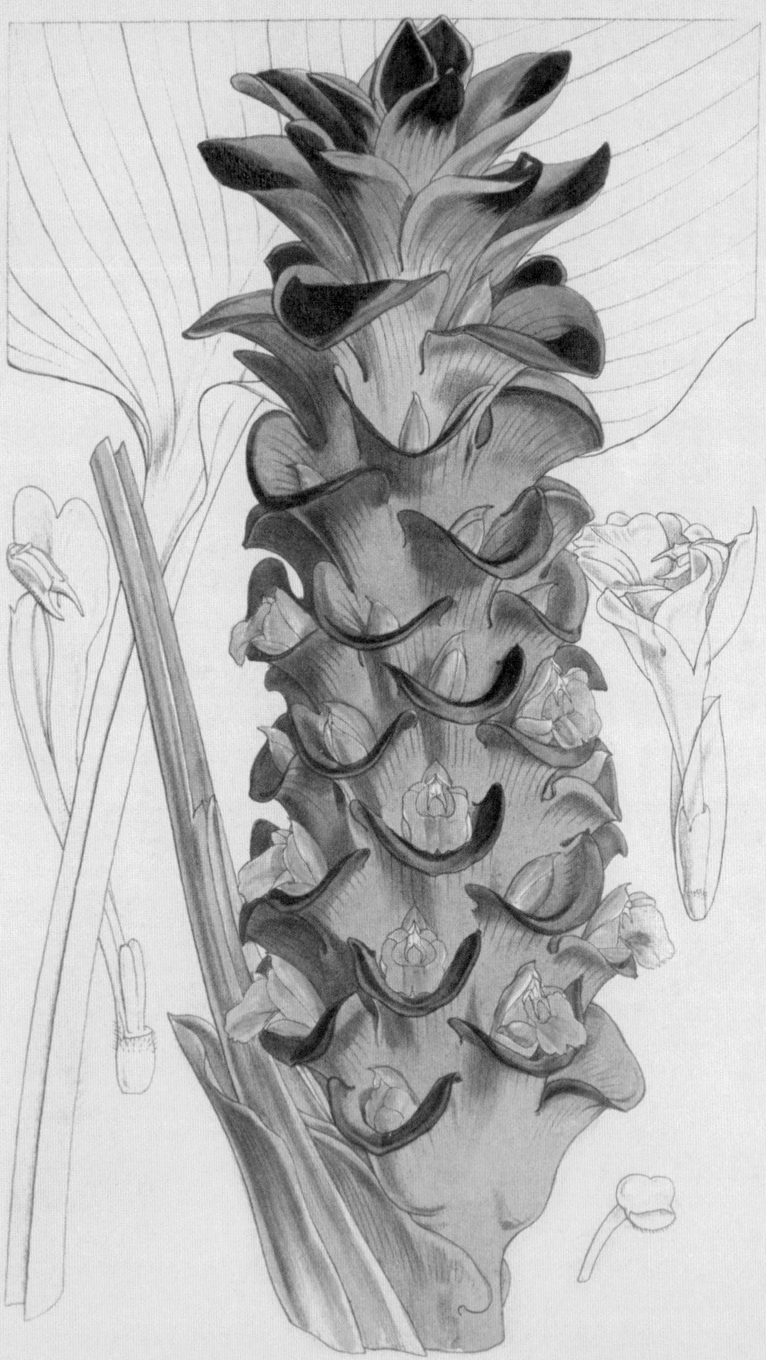

5596

5273

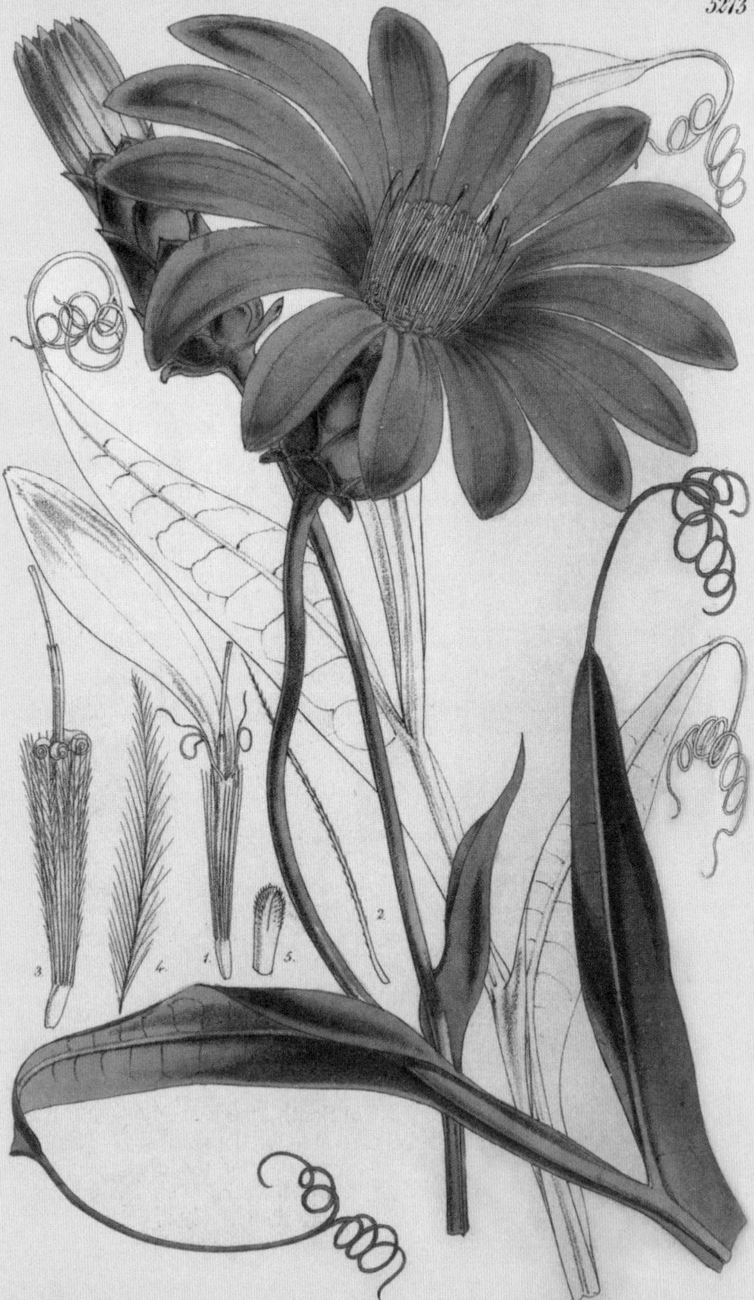

W. Fitch, del et lith.

Vincent Brooks, Imp.

36

W. Fitch, del et lith.

Vincent, Brooks, Imp.

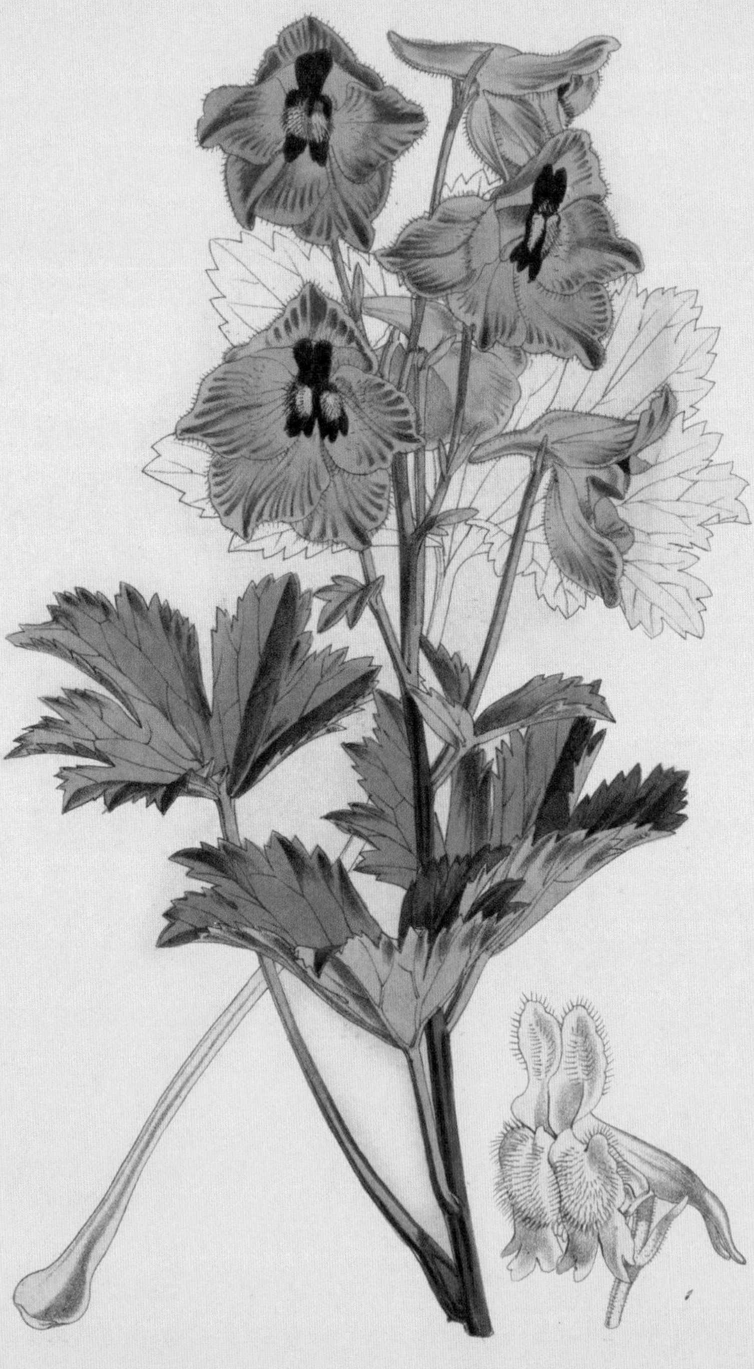

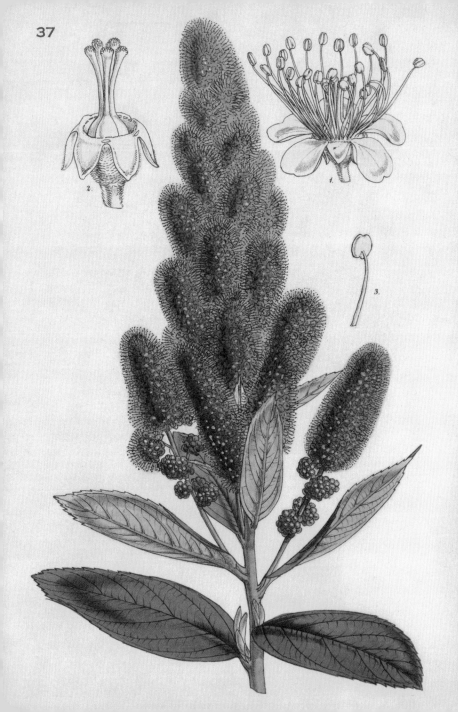

37

1.

2

1.   2.

W Fitch del et lith.

Vincent Brooks, Imp.

W.Fitch, del. et lith.

Vincent. Brooks, Imp.

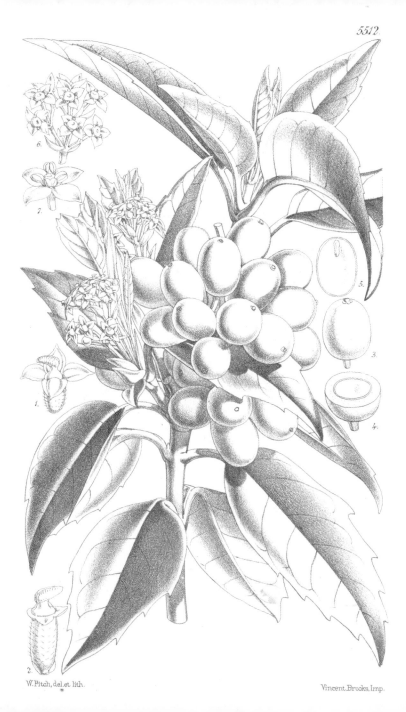

W. Fitch, del. et lith.

Vincent Brooks, Imp.

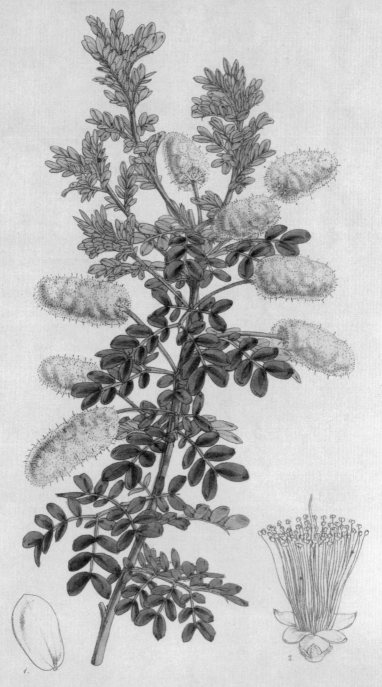

1.
2.

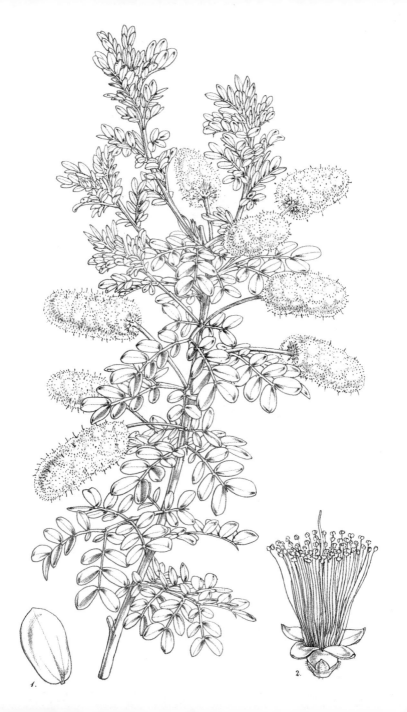

1.

2.

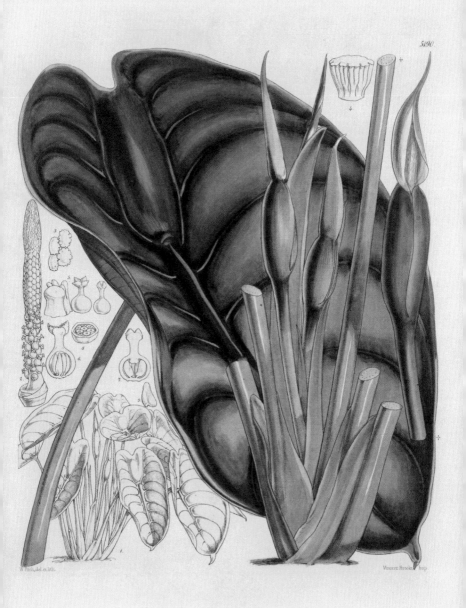

5190

W Fitch, del. et lith.

Vincent Brooks, Imp.

W Fitch, del et lith.

Vincent Brooks Imp.

4469.

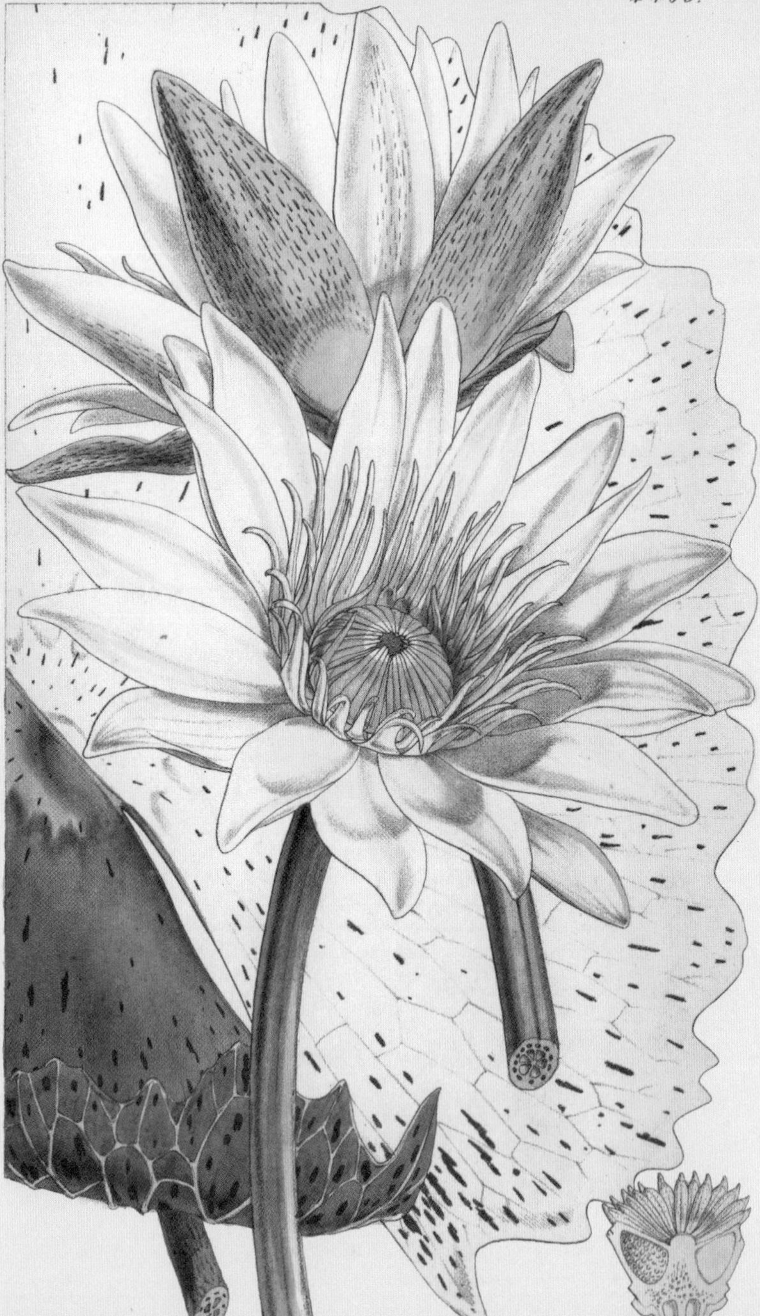

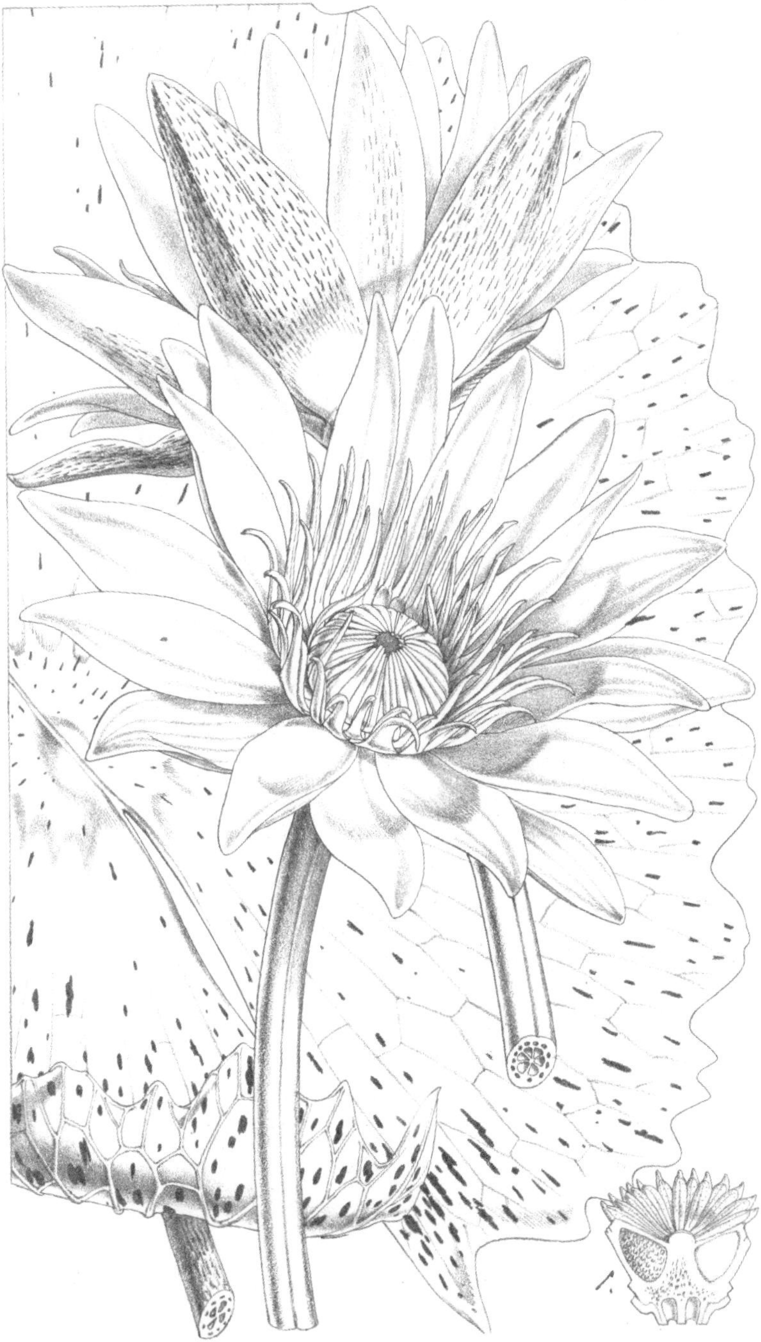
1.

Vincent Brooks, Imp.

W. Fitch, del et lith.

2.

3.

1.

4.

5.

W. Fitch, del et lith.

51

W. Fitch, del. et lith.

Vincent Brooks, Imp.

2.   1.

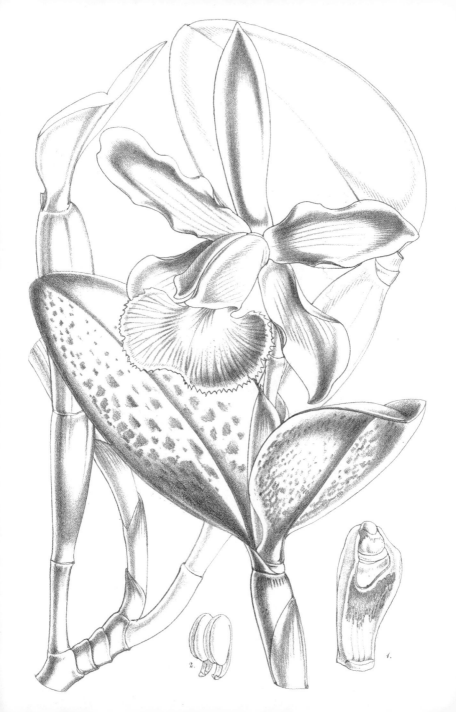

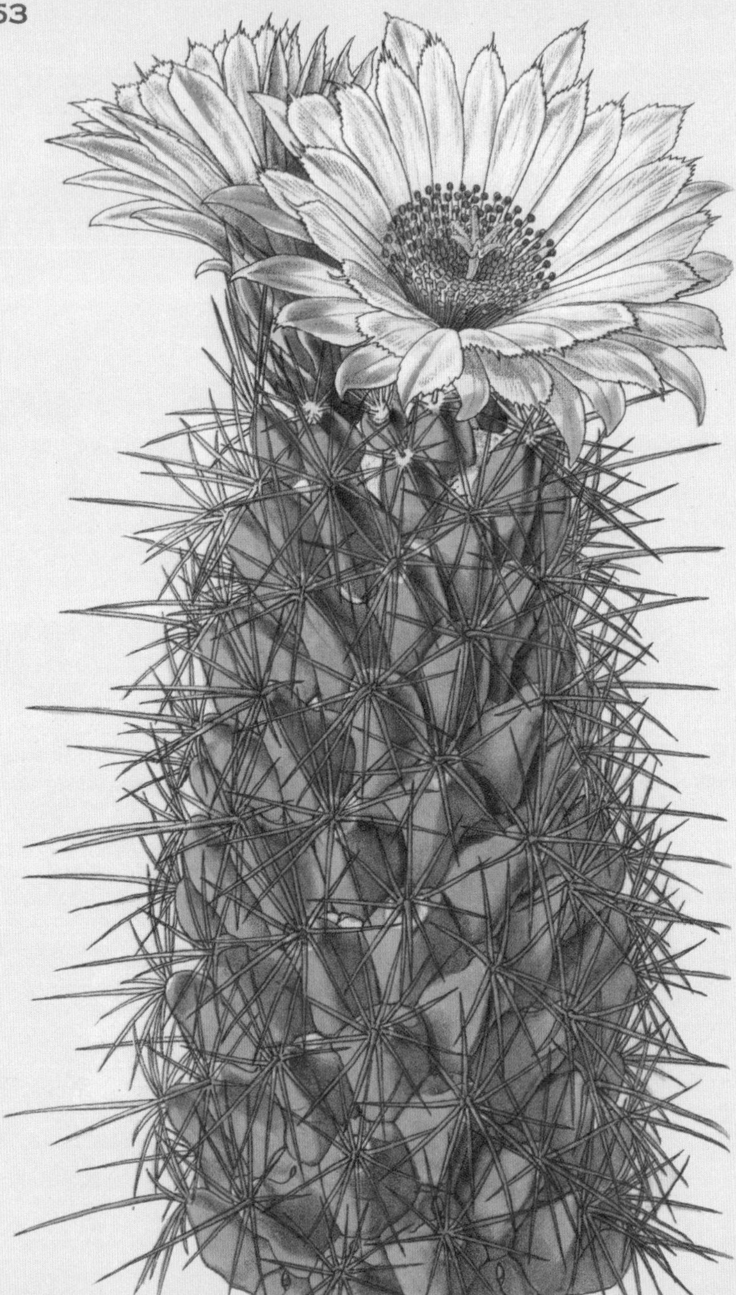

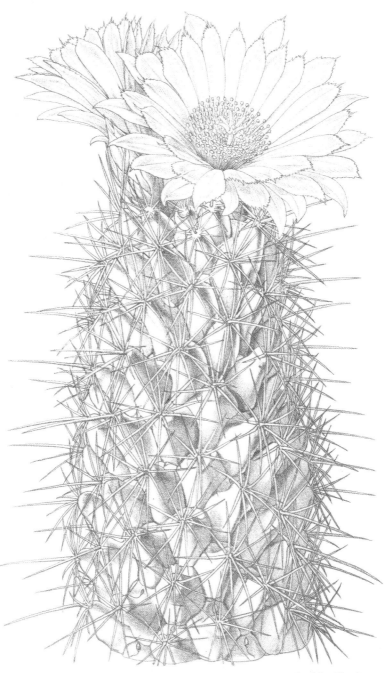

W.Fitch,del.et lith.

Vincent.Brooks, Imp.